G000122837

ABOUT US

The Royal Horticultural Society, the world's leading gardening charity, was founded in 1804 by Sir Joseph Banks and John Wedgwood. Our vision is to enrich everyone's life through plants, and make the UK a greener and more beautiful place. This aspiration underpins all that we do, from inspirational gardens and shows, through our scientific research, to our education and community programmes such as Campaign for School Gardening and Britain in Bloom.
We produce key publications, hold a world-class collection of horticultural books and botanical art, and sell the very best plants and gardening gifts.
The RHS is fundraising £40m to transform our gardens, outreach and education facilities, which includes redeveloping our flagship RHS Garden Wisley and opening a new garden, RHS Garden Bridgewater. We are solely funded by our members, visitors and supporters.
Visit our website www.rhs.org.uk to find out more.

OUR GARDENS
Our five gardens provide great days out for everyone. Each garden offers a unique experience that includes spectacular gardens with interesting walks, ample parking, cafes and restaurants, organised events, a plant centre and gift shop.
To find out more about all of our gardens and what's on, visit: www.rhs.org.uk/gardens.

RHS GARDEN BRIDGEWATER, SALFORD, GREATER MANCHESTER M28 1LF:
Our fifth RHS garden opened in 2021 bringing the historic gardens of Worsley New Hall back to life, providing a stunning new 62 hectare (154 acre) garden in the heart of the North West. Find out more at www.rhs.org.uk/gardens/bridgewater.

RHS GARDEN HARLOW CARR, HARROGATE, NORTH YORKSHIRE HG3 1QB:
Sitting in the beautiful Yorkshire countryside, Harlow Carr has a wide variety of growing landscapes, from running and still water to woodland and wildflower meadows. Visit the Alpine House and wander through the Rhododendron Glade, which is particularly beautiful in the spring.
RHS Garden Harlow Carr: 01423 565 418   Email: harlowcarr@rhs.org.uk

RHS GARDEN HYDE HALL, CHELMSFORD, ESSEX CM3 8RA:
Nestled in the heart of Essex, Hyde Hall has a unique character and charm. This is a dynamic garden with spectacular views that are constantly changing to meet the challenges of the open site and soil conditions.
RHS Garden Hyde Hall: 01245 402019   Email: hydehall@rhs.org.uk

RHS GARDEN ROSEMOOR, GREAT TORRINGTON, DEVON EX38 8PH:
Set in rural North Devon, this garden is truly beautiful, situated within a steep wooded valley. Donated to the RHS in 1988, the gardens and woodland reflect the characteristic style of a West Country garden.
RHS Garden Rosemoor: 01805 624 067   Email: rosemooradmin@rhs.org.uk

RHS GARDEN WISLEY, WOKING, SURREY GU23 6QB:
This is our most established garden and also the base for our scientific activity. Within the gardens you will find the spectacular Glasshouse, which provides a home to many tropical species. This garden is a great destination whatever the season.
RHS Garden Wisley: 01483 224 234   Email: wisley@rhs.org.uk

OUR SHOWS:
RHS shows are the highlight of many a gardener's year and include the RHS Chelsea Flower Show, RHS Hampton Court Palace Garden Festival, and many more.
Find the latest show dates and buy tickets at: www.rhs.org.uk/shows-events

OUR LIBRARIES:
Our libraries hold the world's finest collection of books and printed materials on gardening and outstanding collections of archives, photography and botanical art.
For enquiries about RHS libraries, email: library@rhs.org.uk
For more information, visit: www.rhs.org.uk/education-learning/libraries-at-rhs

ADVICE:
For general, monthly and seasonal advice, information for beginners, ideas for garden designs and topical articles from our expert gardeners, visit: www.rhs.org.uk/advice

MEMBERSHIP:
Make our world-famous gardens your own with unlimited access to our five RHS Gardens.
More than 200 RHS Partner Gardens across the UK for RHS main members to enjoy for free at selected times.

GREAT REASONS TO JOIN:
- Visit all 5 RHS Gardens for the member and a family guest or 2 children
- Monthly subscription to The Garden magazine
- Unlimited, personalised RHS gardening advice
- Regular emails with exclusive member content
- Free entry to over 200 Partner Gardens for the member
- Savings on tickets to RHS Shows

Visit: www.rhs.org.uk/join

For membership enquiries, call 0203 176 5820 (weekdays 9am to 5pm, excluding Bank Holidays) or email membership@rhs.org.uk

Inspiring everyone to grow

© The Royal Horticultural Society

Manufactured under licence granted to Danilo Promotions Ltd by the Royal Horticultural Society

Registered Charity No 222879/SC038262

rhs.org.uk

PERSONAL INFORMATION

Name

Address

Mobile

Email

IN CASE OF EMERGENCY PLEASE CONTACT

Name

Address

Mobile

Doctor

Doctor Telephone

Known Allergies

NOTES

JANUARY

WK	M	T	W	T	F	S	S
52						1	2
1	3	4	5	6	7	8	9
2	10	11	12	13	14	15	16
3	17	18	19	20	21	22	23
4	24	25	26	27	28	29	30
5	31						

FEBRUARY

WK	M	T	W	T	F	S	S
5		1	2	3	4	5	6
6	7	8	9	10	11	12	13
7	14	15	16	17	18	19	20
8	21	22	23	24	25	26	27
9	28						

MARCH

WK	M	T	W	T	F	S	S
9		1	2	3	4	5	6
10	7	8	9	10	11	12	13
11	14	15	16	17	18	19	20
12	21	22	23	24	25	26	27
13	28	29	30	31			

APRIL

WK	M	T	W	T	F	S	S
13					1	2	3
14	4	5	6	7	8	9	10
15	11	12	13	14	15	16	17
16	18	19	20	21	22	23	24
17	25	26	27	28	29	30	

MAY

WK	M	T	W	T	F	S	S
17							1
18	2	3	4	5	6	7	8
19	9	10	11	12	13	14	15
20	16	17	18	19	20	21	22
21	23	24	25	26	27	28	29
22	30	31					

JUNE

WK	M	T	W	T	F	S	S
22			1	2	3	4	5
23	6	7	8	9	10	11	12
24	13	14	15	16	17	18	19
25	20	21	22	23	24	25	26
26	27	28	29	30			

JULY

WK	M	T	W	T	F	S	S
26					1	2	3
27	4	5	6	7	8	9	10
28	11	12	13	14	15	16	17
29	18	19	20	21	22	23	24
30	25	26	27	28	29	30	31

AUGUST

WK	M	T	W	T	F	S	S
31	1	2	3	4	5	6	7
32	8	9	10	11	12	13	14
33	15	16	17	18	19	20	21
34	22	23	24	25	26	27	28
35	29	30	31				

SEPTEMBER

WK	M	T	W	T	F	S	S
35				1	2	3	4
36	5	6	7	8	9	10	11
37	12	13	14	15	16	17	18
38	19	20	21	22	23	24	25
39	26	27	28	29	30		

OCTOBER

WK	M	T	W	T	F	S	S
39						1	2
40	3	4	5	6	7	8	9
41	10	11	12	13	14	15	16
42	17	18	19	20	21	22	23
43	24	25	26	27	28	29	30
44	31						

NOVEMBER

WK	M	T	W	T	F	S	S
44		1	2	3	4	5	6
45	7	8	9	10	11	12	13
46	14	15	16	17	18	19	20
47	21	22	23	24	25	26	27
48	28	29	30				

DECEMBER

WK	M	T	W	T	F	S	S
48				1	2	3	4
49	5	6	7	8	9	10	11
50	12	13	14	15	16	17	18
51	19	20	21	22	23	24	25
52	26	27	28	29	30	31	

2023

JANUARY

WK	M	T	W	T	F	S	S
52							1
1	2	3	4	5	6	7	8
2	9	10	11	12	13	14	15
3	16	17	18	19	20	21	22
4	23	24	25	26	27	28	29
5	30	31					

FEBRUARY

WK	M	T	W	T	F	S	S
5			1	2	3	4	5
6	6	7	8	9	10	11	12
7	13	14	15	16	17	18	19
8	20	21	22	23	24	25	26
9	27	28					

MARCH

WK	M	T	W	T	F	S	S
9			1	2	3	4	5
10	6	7	8	9	10	11	12
11	13	14	15	16	17	18	19
12	20	21	22	23	24	25	26
13	27	28	29	30	31		

APRIL

WK	M	T	W	T	F	S	S
13						1	2
14	3	4	5	6	7	8	9
15	10	11	12	13	14	15	16
16	17	18	19	20	21	22	23
17	24	25	26	27	28	29	30

MAY

WK	M	T	W	T	F	S	S
18	1	2	3	4	5	6	7
19	8	9	10	11	12	13	14
20	15	16	17	18	19	20	21
21	22	23	24	25	26	27	28
22	29	30	31				

JUNE

WK	M	T	W	T	F	S	S
22				1	2	3	4
23	5	6	7	8	9	10	11
24	12	13	14	15	16	17	18
25	19	20	21	22	23	24	25
26	26	27	28	29	30		

JULY

WK	M	T	W	T	F	S	S
26						1	2
27	3	4	5	6	7	8	9
28	10	11	12	13	14	15	16
29	17	18	19	20	21	22	23
30	24	25	26	27	28	29	30
31	31						

AUGUST

WK	M	T	W	T	F	S	S
31		1	2	3	4	5	6
32	7	8	9	10	11	12	13
33	14	15	16	17	18	19	20
34	21	22	23	24	25	26	27
35	28	29	30	31			

SEPTEMBER

WK	M	T	W	T	F	S	S
35					1	2	3
36	4	5	6	7	8	9	10
37	11	12	13	14	15	16	17
38	18	19	20	21	22	23	24
39	25	26	27	28	29	30	

OCTOBER

WK	M	T	W	T	F	S	S
39							1
40	2	3	4	5	6	7	8
41	9	10	11	12	13	14	15
42	16	17	18	19	20	21	22
43	23	24	25	26	27	28	29
44	30	31					

NOVEMBER

WK	M	T	W	T	F	S	S
44			1	2	3	4	5
45	6	7	8	9	10	11	12
46	13	14	15	16	17	18	19
47	20	21	22	23	24	25	26
48	27	28	29	30			

DECEMBER

WK	M	T	W	T	F	S	S
48					1	2	3
49	4	5	6	7	8	9	10
50	11	12	13	14	15	16	17
51	18	19	20	21	22	23	24
52	25	26	27	28	29	30	31

	2022
New Year's Day	Jan 1
New Year's Day Holiday	Jan 3
Bank Holiday (Scotland)	Jan 4
Chinese New Year (Tiger)	Feb 1
Valentine's Day	Feb 14
St. David's Day (Wales) / Shrove Tuesday	Mar 1
St. Patrick's Day	Mar 17
Daylight Saving Time Starts / Mothering Sunday	Mar 27
Ramadan Begins	Apr 2
Good Friday / Passover Begins	Apr 15
Easter Sunday	Apr 17
Easter Monday	Apr 18
St. George's Day	Apr 23
Early May Bank Holiday	May 2
Queen's Platinum Jubilee Bank Holiday	Jun 2
Queen's Platinum Jubilee Bank Holiday	Jun 3
Father's Day	Jun 19
Battle of the Boyne (Northern Ireland)	Jul 12
Islamic New Year Begins	Jul 29
Summer Bank Holiday (Scotland)	Aug 1
Summer Bank Holiday (ENG, NIR, WAL)	Aug 29
The United Nations International Day of Peace	Sept 21
Rosh Hashanah (Jewish New Year) Begins	Sept 25
Yom Kippur Begins	Oct 4
World Mental Health Day	Oct 10
Diwali	Oct 24
Daylight Saving Time Ends	Oct 30
Halloween	Oct 31
Guy Fawkes Night	Nov 5
Remembrance Sunday	Nov 13
St. Andrew's Day (Scotland)	Nov 30
Christmas Day	Dec 25
Boxing Day	Dec 26
Bank Holiday	Dec 27
New Year's Eve	Dec 31

PLANNER 2022 ────────────

JANUARY	FEBRUARY	MARCH
1 S	1 T	1 T
2 S	2 W	2 W
3 M	3 T	3 T
4 T	4 F	4 F
5 W	5 S	5 S
6 T	6 S	6 S
7 F	7 M	7 M
8 S	8 T	8 T
9 S	9 W	9 W
10 M	10 T	10 T
11 T	11 F	11 F
12 W	12 S	12 S
13 T	13 S	13 S
14 F	14 M	14 M
15 S	15 T	15 T
16 S	16 W	16 W
17 M	17 T	17 T
18 T	18 F	18 F
19 W	19 S	19 S
20 T	20 S	20 S
21 F	21 M	21 M
22 S	22 T	22 T
23 S	23 W	23 W
24 M	24 T	24 T
25 T	25 F	25 F
26 W	26 S	26 S
27 T	27 S	27 S
28 F	28 M	28 M
29 S		29 T
30 S		30 W
31 M		31 T

PLANNER 2022

APRIL	MAY	JUNE
1 F	1 S	1 W
2 S	2 M	2 T
3 S	3 T	3 F
4 M	4 W	4 S
5 T	5 T	5 S
6 W	6 F	6 M
7 T	7 S	7 T
8 F	8 S	8 W
9 S	9 M	9 T
10 S	10 T	10 F
11 M	11 W	11 S
12 T	12 T	12 S
13 W	13 F	13 M
14 T	14 S	14 T
15 F	15 S	15 W
16 S	16 M	16 T
17 S	17 T	17 F
18 M	18 W	18 S
19 T	19 T	19 S
20 W	20 F	20 M
21 T	21 S	21 T
22 F	22 S	22 W
23 S	23 M	23 T
24 S	24 T	24 F
25 M	25 W	25 S
26 T	26 T	26 S
27 W	27 F	27 M
28 T	28 S	28 T
29 F	29 S	29 W
30 S	30 M	30 T
	31 T	

PLANNER 2022

JULY	AUGUST	SEPTEMBER
1 F	1 M	1 T
2 S	2 T	2 F
3 S	3 W	3 S
4 M	4 T	4 S
5 T	5 F	5 M
6 W	6 S	6 T
7 T	7 S	7 W
8 F	8 M	8 T
9 S	9 T	9 F
10 S	10 W	10 S
11 M	11 T	11 S
12 T	12 F	12 M
13 W	13 S	13 T
14 T	14 S	14 W
15 F	15 M	15 T
16 S	16 T	16 F
17 S	17 W	17 S
18 M	18 T	18 S
19 T	19 F	19 M
20 W	20 S	20 T
21 T	21 S	21 W
22 F	22 M	22 T
23 S	23 T	23 F
24 S	24 W	24 S
25 M	25 T	25 S
26 T	26 F	26 M
27 W	27 S	27 T
28 T	28 S	28 W
29 F	29 M	29 T
30 S	30 T	30 F
31 S	31 W	

PLANNER 2022

OCTOBER	NOVEMBER	DECEMBER
1 S	1 T	1 T
2 S	2 W	2 F
3 M	3 T	3 S
4 T	4 F	4 S
5 W	5 S	5 M
6 T	6 S	6 T
7 F	7 M	7 W
8 S	8 T	8 T
9 S	9 W	9 F
10 M	10 T	10 S
11 T	11 F	11 S
12 W	12 S	12 M
13 T	13 S	13 T
14 F	14 M	14 W
15 S	15 T	15 T
16 S	16 W	16 F
17 M	17 T	17 S
18 T	18 F	18 S
19 W	19 S	19 M
20 T	20 S	20 T
21 F	21 M	21 W
22 S	22 T	22 T
23 S	23 W	23 F
24 M	24 T	24 S
25 T	25 F	25 S
26 W	26 S	26 M
27 T	27 S	27 T
28 F	28 M	28 W
29 S	29 T	29 T
30 S	30 W	30 F
31 M		31 S

PRIORITIES _____

PRIORITIES

JANUARY

Camellia sasanqua cultivar in Oakwood, RHS Garden Wisley © RHS / Joanna Kossak

DEC 2021 / JAN 2022

27 Monday   Bank Holiday

---

28 Tuesday   Bank Holiday

---

29 Wednesday

---

30 Thursday

---

31 Friday   New Year's Eve

---

01 Saturday   New Year's Day

---

02 Sunday

Begonia soli-mutata © RHS / Joanna Kossak

JANUARY 2022

New Year's Day Holiday

Monday 03

Bank Holiday (Scotland)

Tuesday 04

Wednesday 05

Thursday 06

Friday 07

Saturday 08

Sunday 09

Cornus alba 'Sibirica' © RHS / Joanna Kossak

J

JANUARY 2022

10 Monday

---

11 Tuesday

---

12 Wednesday

---

13 Thursday

---

14 Friday

---

15 Saturday

---

16 Sunday

Erica carnea 'Corinna' © RHS / Joanna Kossak

JANUARY 2022

Monday 17

Tuesday 18

Wednesday 19

Thursday 20

Friday 21

Saturday 22

Sunday 23

Hamamelis mollis in the Sandstone Rock Garden, RHS Garden Harlow Car © RHS / Neil Hepworth

JANUARY 2022

24 Monday

25 Tuesday

26 Wednesday

27 Thursday

28 Friday

29 Saturday

30 Sunday

Hebe 'Heartbreaker' © RHS / Joanna Kossak

FEBRUARY

Viburnum tinus 'Grandiflora' © RHS / Joanna Kossak

JAN/FEB 2022

31 Monday

01 Tuesday   Chinese New Year (Tiger)

02 Wednesday

03 ·Thursday

04 Friday

05 Saturday

06 Sunday

Crocus vernus © RHS / Barry Phillips

FEBRUARY 2022

Monday 07

Tuesday 08

Wednesday 09

Thursday 10

Friday 11

Saturday 12

Sunday 13

Prunus × *juddii* © RHS / Joanna Kossak

FEBRUARY 2022

14 Monday

15 Tuesday

16 Wednesday

17 Thursday

18 Friday

19 Saturday

20 Sunday

Edgeworthia chrysantha 'Grandiflora' in the Winter Garden, RHS Garden Rosemoor © RHS / Jason Ingram

F

FEBRUARY 2022

Monday 21

Tuesday 22

Wednesday 23

Thursday 24

Friday 25

Saturday 26

Sunday 27

F

Helleborus Walberton's Rosemary = 'Walhero' © RHS / Tim Sandall

MARCH

FEB/MAR 2022

Monday 28

St. David's Day (Wales) / Shrove Tuesday

Tuesday 01

M

Wednesday 02

Thursday 03

Friday 04

Saturday 05

Sunday 06

Narcissus bulbocodium in Lady Anne's Arboretum, RHS Garden Rosemoor © RHS / Jason Ingram

MARCH 2022

07 Monday

08 Tuesday

09 Wednesday

10 Thursday

11 Friday

12 Saturday

13 Sunday

Camellia japonica 'Pink Dawn' © RHS / Joanna Kossak

MARCH 2022

Monday 14

Tuesday 15

M

Wednesday 16

St. Patrick's Day   Thursday 17

Friday 18

Saturday 19

Sunday 20

Tulipa, RHS Garden Harlow Carr © RHS / Neil Hepworth

MARCH 2022

21 Monday

---

22 Tuesday

---

23 Wednesday

---

24 Thursday

---

25 Friday

---

26 Saturday

---

27 Sunday   Daylight Saving Time Starts / Mothering Sunday

Camellia x *williamsii* 'Donation' in the Winter Garden, RHS Garden Rosemoor © RHS / Jason Ingram

APRIL

Erysimum 'Poem Lavender' © RHS / Joanna Kossak

MAR/APR 2022

28 Monday

29 Tuesday

30 Wednesday

31 Thursday

01 Friday

02 Saturday   Ramadan Begins

03 Sunday

Stachyurus chinensis 'Celina' in the Winter Garden, RHS Garden Rosemoor © RHS / Jason Ingram

APRIL 2022

Monday 04

Tuesday 05

A

Wednesday 06

Thursday 07

Friday 08

Saturday 09

Sunday 10

Erica carnea 'John Pook'   © RHS / Joanna Kossak

APRIL 2022

11 Monday

12 Tuesday

13 Wednesday

14 Thursday

15 Friday   Good Friday / Passover Begins

16 Saturday

17 Sunday   Easter Sunday

Narcissus 'Jack Snipe' and *Helleborus* x *hybridus* in the Winter Garden, RHS Garden Rosemoor © RHS / Jason Ingram

A

APRIL 2022

Easter Monday

Monday 18

Tuesday 19

A

Wednesday 20

Thursday 21

Friday 22

St. George's Day

Saturday 23

Sunday 24

Trillium chloropetalum var. *giganteum* RHS Garden Harlow Carr © RHS / Neil Hepworth

MAY

Bergenia 'Pugsley's Pink' with rhododendron in the Woodland Garden, RHS Garden Hyde Hall © RHS / Neil Hepworth

APR/MAY 2022

Monday 25

Tuesday 26

M

Wednesday 27

Thursday 28

Friday 29

Saturday 30

Sunday 01

Trillium luteum with *Tiarella* 'Spring Symphony', RHS Garden Harlow Carr © RHS / Neil Hepworth

MAY 2022

02 Monday

03 Tuesday

04 Wednesday

05 Thursday

06 Friday

07 Saturday

08 Sunday

Tulipa 'Kingsblood' with *Tulipa* 'Queen of Night' and *Tulipa* 'Dordogne' in the Cottage Garden, RHS Garden Hyde Hall
© RHS / Neil Hepworth

MAY 2022

Monday 09

Tuesday 10

Wednesday 11

M

Thursday 12

Friday 13

Saturday 14

Sunday 15

Centaurea montana 'Purple Heart' in the Cottage Garden, RHS Garden Hyde Hall © RHS / Neil Hepworth

MAY 2022

16 Monday

17 Tuesday

18 Wednesday

19 Thursday

20 Friday

21 Saturday

22 Sunday

Rhododendron 'Arctic Glow' and ***Brunnera macrophylla*** 'Jack Frost', RHS Garden Rosemoor © RHS / Jason Ingram

MAY 2022

Monday 23

Tuesday 24

Wednesday 25

Thursday 26

Friday 27

Saturday 28

Sunday 29

Primulas in the Rock Gully, RHS Garden Rosemoor © RHS / Jason Ingram

JUNE

Crocosmia in the Glasshouse Landscape, RHS Garden Wisley © RHS / Joanna Kossak

MAY/JUN 2022

Monday 30

Tuesday 31

Wednesday 01

J

Queen's Platinum Jubilee Bank Holiday   Thursday 02

Queen's Platinum Jubilee Bank Holiday   Friday 03

Saturday 04

Sunday 05

Asphodeline liburnica © RHS / Joanna Kossak

JUNE 2022

06 Monday

07 Tuesday

08 Wednesday

09 Thursday

10 Friday

11 Saturday

12 Sunday

Meconopsis 'Willie Duncan', RHS Garden Harlow Carr © RHS / Neil Hepworth

JUNE 2022

Monday 13

Tuesday 14

Wednesday 15

J

Thursday 16

Friday 17

Saturday 18

Father's Day

Sunday 19

Astrantia major 'Rosensinfonie' © RHS / Joanna Kossak

JUNE 2022

20 Monday

21 Tuesday

22 Wednesday

23 Thursday

24 Friday

25 Saturday

26 Sunday

Alliums in the Main Borders, RHS Garden Harlow Carr © RHS / Neil Hepworth

J

JULY

Clematis 'Barbara Harrington' © RHS / Joanna Kossak

JUN/JUL 2022

27 Monday

28 Tuesday

29 Wednesday

30 Thursday

01 Friday

02 Saturday

03 Sunday

The Cool Garden, RHS Garden Rosemoor © RHS / Jason Ingram

JULY 2022

Monday 04

Tuesday 05

Wednesday 06

Thursday 07

J

Friday 08

Saturday 09

Sunday 10

Nymphaea 'Charlene Strawn' © RHS / Paul Debois

JULY 2022

11 Monday

12 Tuesday   Battle of the Boyne (Northern Ireland)

13 Wednesday

14 Thursday

15 Friday

16 Saturday

17 Sunday

Rosa Young Lycidas = 'Ausvibrant' in the Rose Garden, RHS Garden Hyde Hall © RHS / Neil Hepworth

JULY 2022

Monday 18

Tuesday 19

Wednesday 20

Thursday 21

Friday 22

Saturday 23

Sunday 24

J

Astilbe 'Weisse Perle' (× *arendsii*) © RHS / Joanna Kossak

JULY 2022

Monday 25

Tuesday 26

Wednesday 27

Thursday 28

Islamic New Year Begins   Friday 29

Saturday 30

Sunday 31

AUGUST

Zantedeschia 'Flame'   © RHS / Joanna Kossak

AUGUST 2022

01 Monday   Summer Bank Holiday (Scotland)

---

02 Tuesday

---

03 Wednesday

---

04 Thursday

---

05 Friday

---

06 Saturday

---

07 Sunday

Hydrangea aspera Hot Chocolate = 'Haopr012' © RHS / Joanna Kossak

AUGUST 2022

Monday 08

Tuesday 09

Wednesday 10

Thursday 11

A

Friday 12

Saturday 13

Sunday 14

Prunus domestica 'Oullins Gage' © RHS / Tim Sandall

AUGUST 2022

15 Monday

16 Tuesday

17 Wednesday

18 Thursday

19 Friday

20 Saturday

21 Sunday

Rosa Queen Mother = 'Korquemu', RHS Garden Rosemoor © RHS / Jason Ingram

AUGUST 2022

Monday 22

Tuesday 23

Wednesday 24

Thursday 25

A

Friday 26

Saturday 27

Sunday 28

Eryngium planum 'Blue Glitter' © RHS / Joanna Kossak

SEPTEMBER

Rosa Absolutely Fabulous = 'Wekvossutono', RHS Garden Rosemoor © RHS / Jason Ingram

AUG/SEP 2022

Summer Bank Holiday (ENG, NIR, WAL)

Monday 29

Tuesday 30

Wednesday 31

Thursday 01

Friday 02

S

Saturday 03

Sunday 04

Salvia in the Main Borders, RHS Garden Harlow Carr © RHS / Neil Hepworth

SEPTEMBER 2022

05 Monday

06 Tuesday

07 Wednesday

08 Thursday

09 Friday

10 Saturday

11 Sunday

Harvested courgettes and beans from the RHS Garden Wisley Community Allotments © RHS / Paul Debois

SEPTEMBER 2022

Monday 12

Tuesday 13

Wednesday 14

Thursday 15

Friday 16

S

Saturday 17

Sunday 18

Abutilon 'Red Tiger' © RHS / Mark Bolton

SEPTEMBER 2022

19 Monday

20 Tuesday

21 Wednesday   The United Nations International Day of Peace

22 Thursday

23 Friday

24 Saturday

25 Sunday   Rosh Hashanah (Jewish New Year) Begins

Prunus domestica 'Giant Prune' © RHS / Tim Sandall

OCTOBER

SEP/OCT 2022

26 Monday

27 Tuesday

28 Wednesday

29 Thursday

30 Friday

01 Saturday

02 Sunday

Dahlia 'Sights of Summer' © RHS / Joanna Kossak

OCTOBER 2022

Monday 03

Yom Kippur Begins

Tuesday 04

Wednesday 05

Thursday 06

Friday 07

Saturday 08

Sunday 09

Helianthus 'Sunfinity' © RHS / Joanna Kossak

OCTOBER 2022

10 Monday

---

11 Tuesday

---

12 Wednesday

---

13 Thursday

---

14 Friday

---

15 Saturday

---

16 Sunday

Harvested vegetable crops at Redhill Allotments, RHS Community Outreach project with Surrey Care Trust © RHS / Helen Yates

OCTOBER 2022

Monday 17

Tuesday 18

Wednesday 19

Thursday 20

Friday 21

O

Saturday 22

Sunday 23

Passiflora 'Snow Queen' © RHS

OCTOBER 2022

24 Monday

Diwali

---

25 Tuesday

---

26 Wednesday

---

27 Thursday

---

28 Friday

---

29 Saturday

---

30 Sunday

Daylight Saving Time Ends

Silene laciniata © RHS / Joanna Kossak

NOVEMBER

Fountain Centre Garden, St. Luke's Cancer Centre, Royal Surrey County Hospital, Guildford in Bloom © RHS / Helen Yates

OCT/NOV 2022

31 Monday

Halloween

01 Tuesday

02 Wednesday

03 Thursday

04 Friday

05 Saturday

Guy Fawkes Night

06 Sunday

Pteris umbrosa © RHS

NOVEMBER 2022

Monday 07

Tuesday 08

Wednesday 09

Thursday 10

Friday 11

Saturday 12

Remembrance Sunday

Sunday 13

N

Osteospermum Purple Sun = 'Kleoe19396' © RHS / Joanna Kossak

NOVEMBER 2022

14 Monday

15 Tuesday

16 Wednesday

17 Thursday

18 Friday

19 Saturday

20 Sunday

Philodendron melanochrysum © RHS / Joanna Kossak

NOVEMBER 2022

Monday 21

Tuesday 22

Wednesday 23

Thursday 24

Friday 25

Saturday 26

Sunday 27

Berberis thunbergii f. *atropurpurea* 'Golden Ring' in the Foliage and Plantsman's Garden, RHS Garden Rosemoor.
© RHS / Jason Ingram

DECEMBER

NOV/DEC 2022

Monday 28

Tuesday 29

St. Andrew's Day (Scotland)   Wednesday 30

Thursday 01

Friday 02

Saturday 03

D

Sunday 04

Kalanchoe Favorita Vada Mae © RHS

DECEMBER 2022

05 Monday

06 Tuesday

07 Wednesday

08 Thursday

09 Friday

10 Saturday

11 Sunday

Sarcococca confusa © RHS / Mark Winwood

DECEMBER 2022

Monday 12

Tuesday 13

Wednesday 14

Thursday 15

Friday 16

Saturday 17

Sunday 18

D

Taxus baccata 'David' © RHS / Joanna Kossak

DECEMBER 2022

19 Monday

20 Tuesday

21 Wednesday

22 Thursday

23 Friday

24 Saturday

25 Sunday   Christmas Day

Skimmia japonica 'Perosa' © RHS / Joanna Kossak

DEC 2022 / JAN 2023

Boxing Day   Monday 26

Bank Holiday   Tuesday 27

Wednesday 28

Thursday 29

Friday 30

New Year's Eve   Saturday 31

New Year's Day   Sunday 01

J

Polystichum setiferum © RHS / Joanna Kossak

PLANNER 2023 ───────────

JANUARY	FEBRUARY	MARCH
1 S	1 W	1 W
2 M	2 T	2 T
3 T	3 F	3 F
4 W	4 S	4 S
5 T	5 S	5 S
6 F	6 M	6 M
7 S	7 T	7 T
8 S	8 W	8 W
9 M	9 T	9 T
10 T	10 F	10 F
11 W	11 S	11 S
12 T	12 S	12 S
13 F	13 M	13 M
14 S	14 T	14 T
15 S	15 W	15 W
16 M	16 T	16 T
17 T	17 F	17 F
18 W	18 S	18 S
19 T	19 S	19 S
20 F	20 M	20 M
21 S	21 T	21 T
22 S	22 W	22 W
23 M	23 T	23 T
24 T	24 F	24 F
25 W	25 S	25 S
26 T	26 S	26 S
27 F	27 M	27 M
28 S	28 T	28 T
29 S		29 W
30 M		30 T
31 T		31 F

PLANNER 2023

APRIL	MAY	JUNE
1 S	1 M	1 T
2 S	2 T	2 F
3 M	3 W	3 S
4 T	4 T	4 S
5 W	5 F	5 M
6 T	6 S	6 T
7 F	7 S	7 W
8 S	8 M	8 T
9 S	9 T	9 F
10 M	10 W	10 S
11 T	11 T	11 S
12 W	12 F	12 M
13 T	13 S	13 T
14 F	14 S	14 W
15 S	15 M	15 T
16 S	16 T	16 F
17 M	17 W	17 S
18 T	18 T	18 S
19 W	19 F	19 M
20 T	20 S	20 T
21 F	21 S	21 W
22 S	22 M	22 T
23 S	23 T	23 F
24 M	24 W	24 S
25 T	25 T	25 S
26 W	26 F	26 M
27 T	27 S	27 T
28 F	28 S	28 W
29 S	29 M	29 T
30 S	30 T	30 F
	31 W	

PLANNER 2023 —————————

JULY	AUGUST	SEPTEMBER
1 S	1 T	1 F
2 S	2 W	2 S
3 M	3 T	3 S
4 T	4 F	4 M
5 W	5 S	5 T
6 T	6 S	6 W
7 F	7 M	7 T
8 S	8 T	8 F
9 S	9 W	9 S
10 M	10 T	10 S
11 T	11 F	11 M
12 W	12 S	12 T
13 T	13 S	13 W
14 F	14 M	14 T
15 S	15 T	15 F
16 S	16 W	16 S
17 M	17 T	17 S
18 T	18 F	18 M
19 W	19 S	19 T
20 T	20 S	20 W
21 F	21 M	21 T
22 S	22 T	22 F
23 S	23 W	23 S
24 M	24 T	24 S
25 T	25 F	25 M
26 W	26 S	26 T
27 T	27 S	27 W
28 F	28 M	28 T
29 S	29 T	29 F
30 S	30 W	30 S
31 M	31 T	

PLANNER 2023

OCTOBER	NOVEMBER	DECEMBER
1 S	1 W	1 F
2 M	2 T	2 S
3 T	3 F	3 S
4 W	4 S	4 M
5 T	5 S	5 T
6 F	6 M	6 W
7 S	7 T	7 T
8 S	8 W	8 F
9 M	9 T	9 S
10 T	10 F	10 S
11 W	11 S	11 M
12 T	12 S	12 T
13 F	13 M	13 W
14 S	14 T	14 T
15 S	15 W	15 F
16 M	16 T	16 S
17 T	17 F	17 S
18 W	18 S	18 M
19 T	19 S	19 T
20 F	20 M	20 W
21 S	21 T	21 T
22 S	22 W	22 F
23 M	23 T	23 S
24 T	24 F	24 S
25 W	25 S	25 M
26 T	26 S	26 T
27 F	27 M	27 W
28 S	28 T	28 T
29 S	29 W	29 F
30 M	30 T	30 S
31 T		31 S

ADDRESS/PHONE NUMBERS

Name

Address

Telephone   Mobile

Email

Name

Address

Telephone   Mobile

Email

Name

Address

Telephone   Mobile

Email

Name

Address

Telephone   Mobile

Email

Name

Address

Telephone   Mobile

Email

Name

Address

Telephone   Mobile

Email

Name

Address

Telephone   Mobile

Email

Name

Address

Telephone   Mobile

Email

Name

Address

Telephone   Mobile

Email

Name

Address

Telephone   Mobile

Email

Name

Address

Telephone   Mobile

Email

Name

Address

Telephone   Mobile

Email

Name

Address

Telephone   Mobile

Email

ADDRESS/PHONE NUMBERS

Name

Address

Telephone   Mobile

Email

Name

Address

Telephone   Mobile

Email

Name

Address

Telephone   Mobile

Email

Name

Address

Telephone   Mobile

Email

Name

Address

Telephone   Mobile

Email

Name

Address

Telephone   Mobile

Email

ADDRESS/PHONE NUMBERS

Name

Address

Telephone   Mobile

Email

Name

Address

Telephone   Mobile

Email

Name

Address

Telephone   Mobile

Email

Name

Address

Telephone   Mobile

Email

Name

Address

Telephone   Mobile

Email

Name

Address

Telephone   Mobile

Email

Name

Address

Telephone   Mobile

Email

ADDRESS/PHONE NUMBERS

Name

Address

Telephone   Mobile

Email

Name

Address

Telephone   Mobile

Email

Name

Address

Telephone   Mobile

Email

Name

Address

Telephone   Mobile

Email

Name

Address

Telephone   Mobile

Email

Name

Address

Telephone   Mobile

Email

Name

Address

Telephone   Mobile

Email

Name

Address

Telephone   Mobile

Email

Name

Address

Telephone   Mobile

Email

Name

Address

Telephone   Mobile

Email

Name

Address

Telephone   Mobile

Email

Name

Address

Telephone   Mobile

Email